Charleston, SC
www.PalmettoPublishing.com

Sheriff Joe

Copyright © 2021 by Joe Powell

First Edition

Paperback ISBN: 978-1-63837-117-5
Hardcover ISBN: 978-1-63837-118-2
eBook ISBN: 978-1-63837-119-9

SHERIFF JOE

FROM BULLIES N' STUFF TO MY BADGE & CUFFS

SHERIFF

POWELL

WRITTEN BY SHERIFF JOE POWELL | ILLUSTRATED BY JULIE POWELL

This book is dedicated to my parents. Words cannot begin to describe the appreciation I will forever have for your time, care, sleepless nights, struggles, patience, and most of all, your faith, love and unwavering encouragement that no matter the issues, I could accomplish anything I set my mind to!

A special thank you to my wife, Julie Powell for encouraging me to continue to pursue my goals and dreams. On June 19th, of 2011, she made my biggest dream yet, come true!

Many years ago way down **south,**

Lived a boy named Joe in a little yellow **house.**

1

Now, most kids have a nickname, and Joe did, **too**.

His mom liked to call him her little **"stinker-potter-doo."**

He lived near the bayou with this mom and **dad**,

Oh, but let me tell you about the troubles he **had**.

From an early age Joe had a hard **time**,

But, as you will see, he ended up just **fine!**

He was born with some problems and sounded funny when he **talked**.

He had very flat feet, so he looked funny when he **walked**.

Speech classes helped a little, and thick glasses helped him **see**

Oh, they were so much thicker than the ones worn by you or **me**. 6

Doctors said he would never be able to see well enough to drive a **car**.

Even with his glasses on, he could not see very **far**.

When Joe
would misplace
his glasses,
why you could
surely **bet**

He would be sitting
just inches away from
the television **set!** 8

When he rode his bike, he seemed to do just **fine**.

That is, unless he had to read a street **sign**.

9

The hole in the roof of his mouth that made him talk **strange**

Was repaired when he was little, but he still felt the **pain**.

When Joe was a baby, his mother fed him through a tube in his **belly**.

He could only eat soft foods like mashed potatoes and strawberry **jelly**.

Growing up like this for Joe surely was not very **fun**.

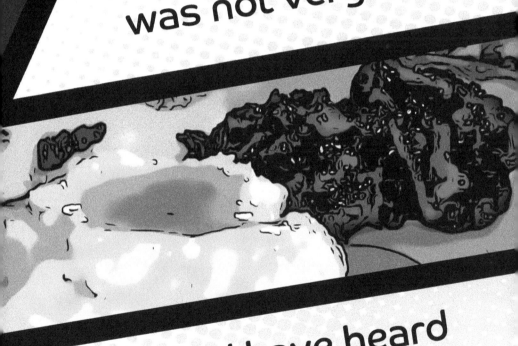

You should have heard people giggle when he would try to **run**!

Every morning at the bus stop, kids would laugh, and he did not know **why**.

They called him four-eyes and other mean things just trying to make him **cry**.

Joe never thought riding the bus was very **cool**

EAST BATON ROUGE PARISH SCHOOLS

Because the children would make fun of him all the way to **school**.

"Flat face, four eyes" they would say while he tried to **ignore**.

This was every day, from the bus to the main school **door**.

15

When he would go in the building, all the kids in his **classes**

Would make fun of the way he talked and his really thick **glasses**.

Kids would push
and shove him
and tell him
he looked
funny.

One day, a bully even
stole his lunch **money.**

Oh, Joe
had a couple
of friends, but
they had
problems
of their
own.

Even
they could
not make
the bullies
leave Joe **alone.**

18

Teachers punished kids for bothering Joe every **day**

But he would just do his work and look the other **way**.

At home he would play by himself and hardly ever go **outside.**

Sometimes even the neighbor kids would make him want to run and **hide**

Although he was made fun of and picked on all the **time,**

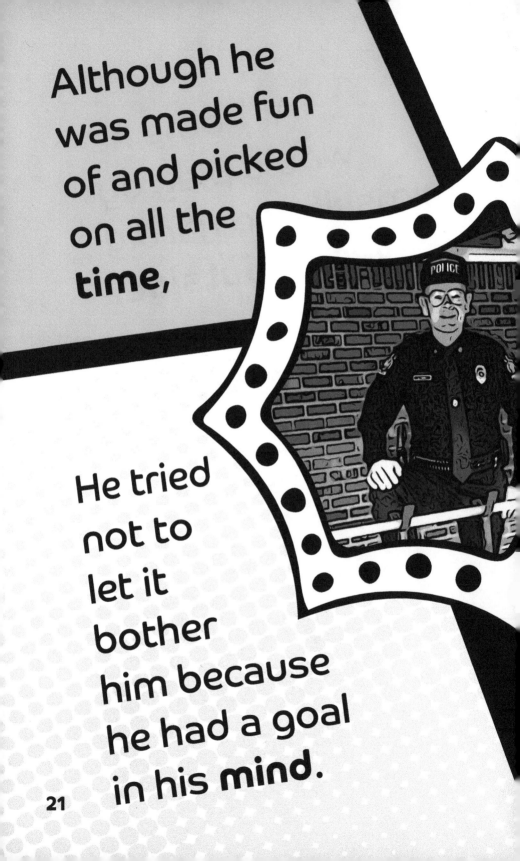

He tried not to let it bother him because he had a goal in his **mind.**

Joe's dad was a police officer and Joe always **knew**

That one day HE would become a police officer, **too**!

When friends and family learned of this dream, they told him it might be **tough**

Because to be a police officer, you must be able to see good **enough!**

They said
"Joe, you can do
anything you want
so don't be **sad**

If you don't become
a police officer just
like your **dad**."

This didn't bother him, but he understood what they were **saying.**

He just kept his head up and never stopped **praying.**

Joe learned
to accept that
he was different
and each and
every **day,**

He would wake up with a
good attitude and look at
his life in a positive **way.**

His dream was his own and nothing would change his **mind.**

He knew deep down that if he believed, it would all work out just **fine.**

Joe would tell the kids what he would do when he got out of **school**.

This made them laugh even more and the bullies told him he was a **fool**.

Joe did not get discouraged and he forgave those who were **mean**.

He just laughed it off because he fully believed in his **dream**.

He loved playing cops and robbers with his little **brother,**

He pretended to arrest everyone, even his **mother!**

Joe carried around a pen and paper, it was with him all the **time**.

If he saw someone do something wrong, they would get a fake ticket and a **fine**.

Everyone knew what
he wanted to do,
he made it very **clear**.

Joe only got
more excited
as High School
drew **near**!

He would lay awake at night just looking up at the **stars.**

He pretended they were chasing each other, like little police **cars.**

As he got older his dream became **stronger**.

When he was done with school, he could not wait any **longer**!

He tried to get police jobs and was proud he never let the bullies **win**.

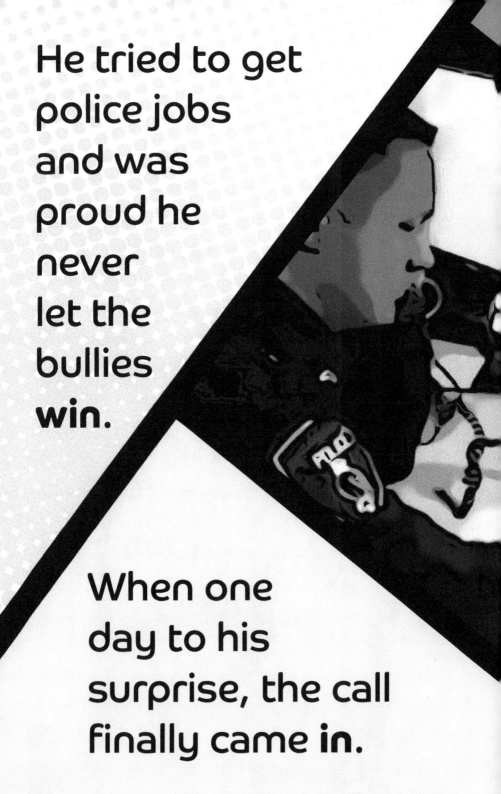

When one day to his surprise, the call finally came **in**.

It was a police
Chief that offered
Joe a chance to
do his very
best,

If
Joe
could
pass the
police
academy,
the Chief would
pin a badge
upon Joe's **chest!**

Remember Joe was flat-footed, and it was hard for him to **run**,

So, the police academy was not sounding very **fun**.

If he was going
to prove himself,
Joe knew what he
had to **do**

Work hard
every day and
set his mind on
making it **through**.

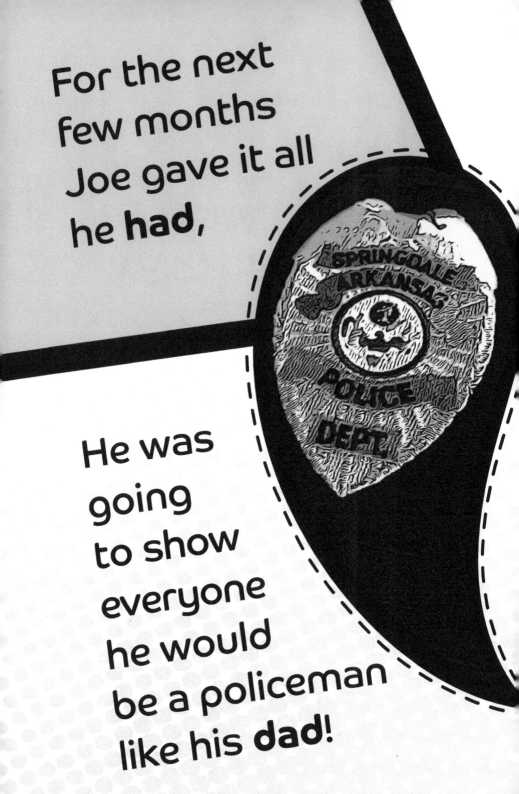

For the next few months Joe gave it all he **had,**

He was going to show everyone he would be a policeman like his **dad!**

Joe was not the fastest in his class, but he never did **quit**.

He would see that badge on an officer's chest, and he knew he wanted **it**.

Nothing could stop him now, so he studied, and he **learned**.

I bet he pushed harder than anyone in that class and, yes, that knowledge was well **earned**.

When the day came to test him on the range and his eyes were still not **right**,

He passed as one of the top in his class and was too happy to sleep that **night**!

Joe became a police officer; his dream had come **true**.

He had done exactly what others said he could not **do**.

He patrolled the streets in disbelief that he had made it this **far.**

Every moment was spent serving his community and shining up his police **car.** 44

Joe was even promoted before his years of service had reached **five.**

He worked at night and arrested people who would drink and **drive.**

Many years
later as Chief
of Police, Joe
had a meeting
with his **crew**.

He told them to
treat everyone with
kindness, no matter
what they **do**.

He told them his story of making it to the **top**.

Forgiving others and staying focused is how he became a **cop**.

"Firm but fair
is our motto"
he would **say,**

"Be fair
with
everyone
as you
patrol
each
day"

As Chief of Police, he wanted more **knowledge**

So, he spent the next 6 years working his job while going to **college**.

Later people in the town asked Joe to run for Sheriff and just so you **know**,

He won the election and ever since has been known as **"Sheriff Joe."**

Sheriff Joe loved to go to the local **park**.

He would spend time with the community, and sometimes sang to them until **dark**.

Oh, I guess you should be aware of one very cool **thing**

Joe is also a DJ and loves to entertain and **sing**.

Yes, he came a long way from being **bullied n' stuff.**

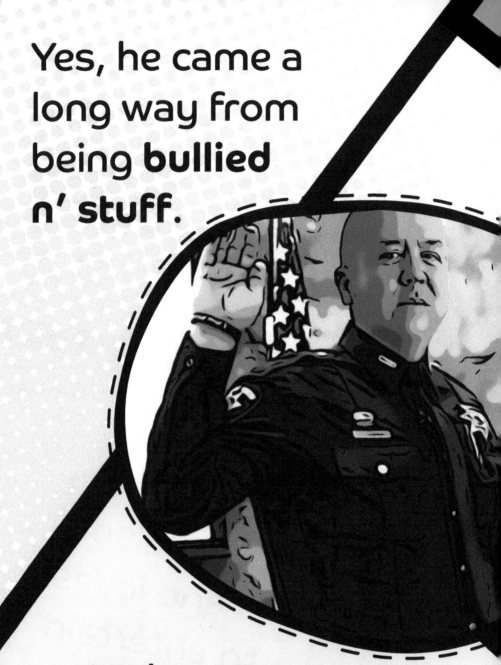

He became a new person when he got his **badge and cuffs.**

He decided to
look after those
who are not
treated
nice

And make
sure that the
bad guys pay
the **price.**

As the sheriff, Joe made it his **rule**

To always take time to walk through the **school**.

He would check
on his little friends
and make sure
every kid **knew**

That no
matter what,
they can do
what they set
their mind **to**.

Joe would sometimes sit in the lunchroom or maybe in a **class,**

Kids might see him in the hallway, ₅₇ waving as they **pass.**

Sheriff Joe believes that no matter what people say or **do**,

Forgive them always because your dreams are not about them, they are about **you**.

Treat everyone
with kindness and
always with respect,
no matter
who they **are**.

Who knows,
one day,
you may be
stopping them
with your own
police **car!**

Focus on your dreams and make friends with those who **care**,

You know, the one's like you, who know they are going **somewhere!**

To wrap this story up, here is what you should **do!**

Ignore the bullies, believe in yourself and go make your dreams come **true!**

Joe Powell has served in almost every division of law enforcement from the mid 90's. (Defying the obstacles that assured his dream of serving would be next to impossible) His career includes years as Chief of Police and County Sheriff in the Texas Panhandle. His education includes: Bachelor of Science in Criminal Justice Administration and a Master of Public Administration. He is a graduate of the Law Enforcement Management Institute of Texas and a trilogy recipient of FBI-LEEDA. He maintains a Master Peace Officer Certification in the State of Texas and holds more than 100 awards, certifications, and commendations. Joe is happily married and could not imagine life without his beautiful wife and kids!

"My passion is helping people live a better, more fulfilled life with no regrets!"

"Time has no reverse."
Sheriff Joe Powell